My first

I can draw...

Farm ANimals

Follow the simple steps
to learn how to draw lots
of charming characters.

•

Tear out the practice pages
to perfect your pictures before
drawing them in the scenes.

Fluffy **sheep**

1

Draw a fluffy body.

2

Add four lines
for the legs.

3

Draw an oval
for the head and
add two ears.

4

Give the sheep
a cute face.

Oinking *pigs*

Try drawing your own . . .

1

Draw a circle
for the body.

2

Add two little legs.

3

Draw two triangles
for the ears and
add a curly tail.

4

Give the muddy pig
two eyes and a
big, pink snout.

Cute **cats**

1

Draw a circle for the head.

2

Add an oval for the body.

3

Draw lines for the tail and legs.

4

Draw two triangles for ears and give the cat a lovely face with whiskers.

Try drawing your own . . .

Happy **puppies**

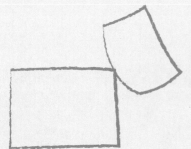

1

Draw a rectangle for the body.

2

Add a head.

3

Draw lines for the legs and tail.

4

Give the cute puppy two ears and a playful face.

Try drawing your own . . .

Clucking **hens**

1

Draw a circle for the body and add a head.

2

Draw a triangle for the tail and add a wing.

3

Draw two lines for the legs and a triangle for the beak.

4

Give the hen a feathery head and an eye.

Try drawing your own . . .

Running rabbits

1
Draw a circle for the head and a slightly larger circle for the body.

2
Add two front legs.

3
Draw two long ears.

4
Draw a fluffy tail and give the rabbit a shy face.

Try drawing your own . . .

Quacking ducks

1

Draw a semicircle for a body.

2

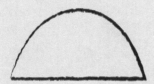

Add a circle for the head.

3

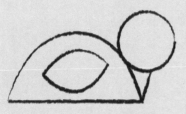

Draw a line for the neck and add a wing.

4

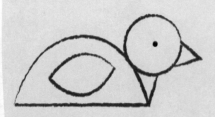

Draw a triangle for the beak and give the duck an eye - quack!

Terrific tractors

1 Draw two big circles for the wheels.

2 Add a rectangle.

Try drawing your own . . .

3 Draw a square for the cabin.

4 Draw small circles inside the big circles.

5 Add a small rectangle for the exhaust.

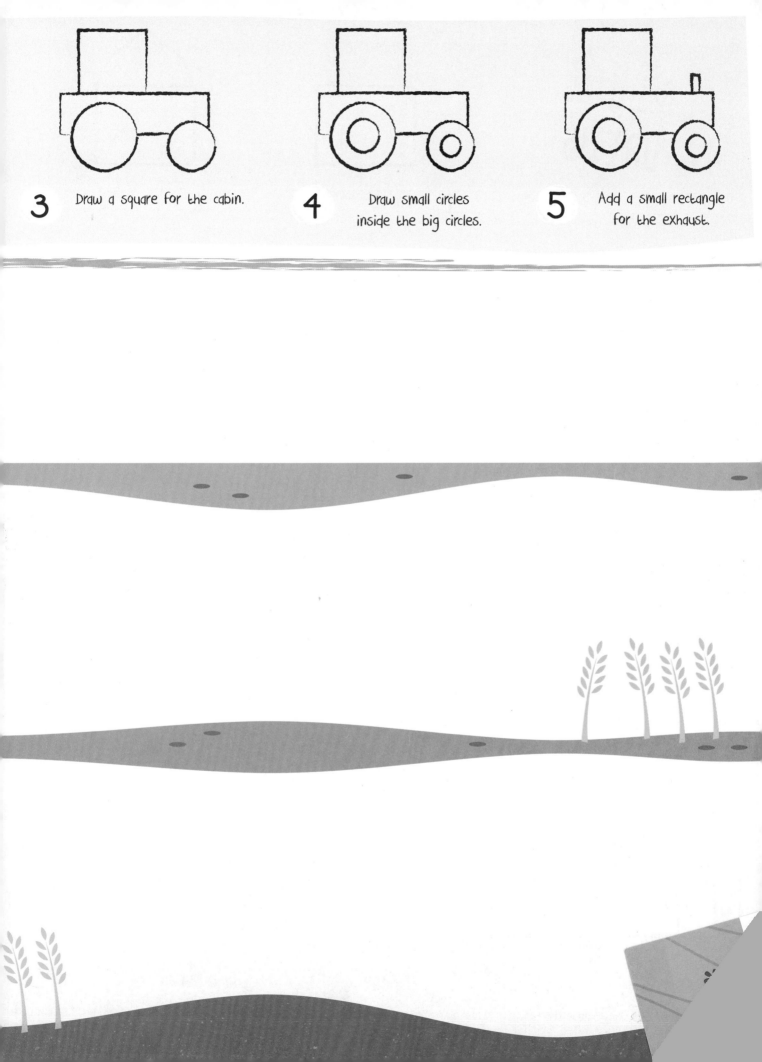

Brilliant barns

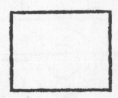

1 Draw a rectangle.

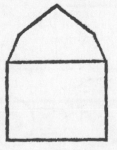

2 Add a roof.

Try drawing your own . . .

3 Draw a square with a line in it for the doors.

4 Draw a circle for the window and add two door handles.

5 Draw two little lines in the window.

Crowing cockerels

1 Draw a semicircle for the body and add the head.

2 Draw a wing.

Try drawing your own . . .

3 Draw two lines for the legs and a little triangle for the beak.

4 Add lines for the feathery tail.

5 Give the cockerel a feathery head and add an eye.

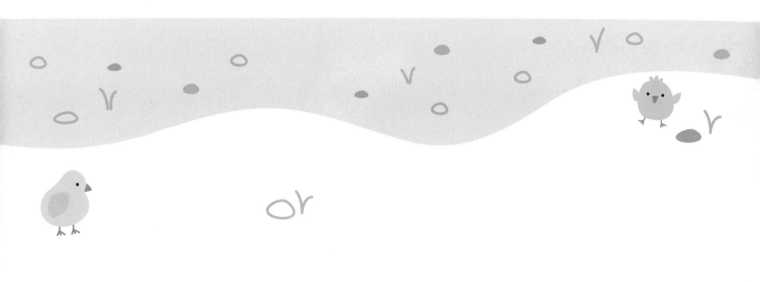

Swimming **swans**

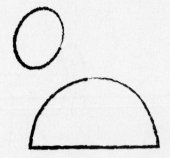

1 Draw an oval for the head and a semicircle for the body.

2 Add a long, curved neck.

Try drawing your own . . .

3 Draw a tail and a beak.

4 Add a wing.

5 Give the swimming swan an eye.

Adorable
donkeys

1 Draw a rectangle for the body.

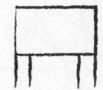

2 Add four straight lines for the legs.

Try drawing your own . . .

3 Draw a head and add a line for the neck.

4 Add two big ears and a line for the tail.

5 Give the donkey a face.

Show **horses**

1

Draw the head and a neck.

2

Add an oval for the body and draw two ears.

3

Draw lines for the legs and tail.

4

Give the happy horse a face and a shaggy mane.

Try drawing your own . . .

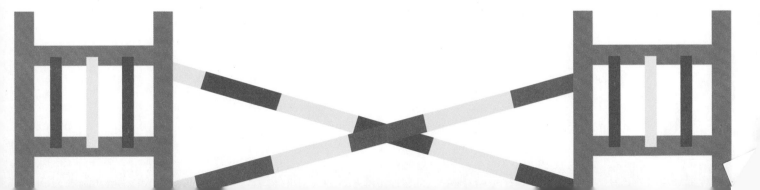

Lively **llamas**

1

Draw a big oval
for the body
and a small oval
for the head.

2

Add a long neck
and two little ears.

3

Draw four lines for
the legs and add
a fluffy tail.

4

Give the llama
two eyes and
a sweet nose.

Try drawing your own . . .

Gorgeous geese

1

Draw an oval
head and add a neck.

2

Draw a
big oval body.

3

Draw triangles for
the beak and tail,
and add two lines
for the legs.

4

Draw a wing
and add an eye
and a nostril.

Try drawing your own . . .

Feathery turkeys

1 Draw a circle for the head and add a neck.

2 Draw an oval for the body and add a bushy tail.

Try drawing your own . . .

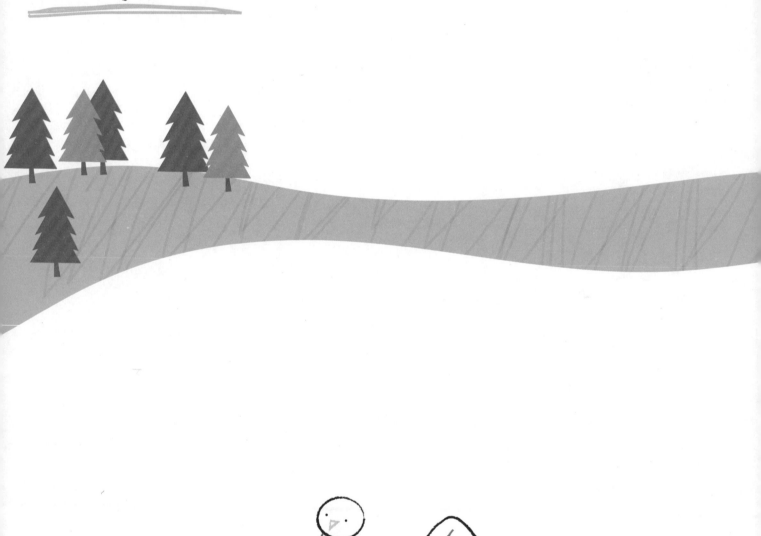

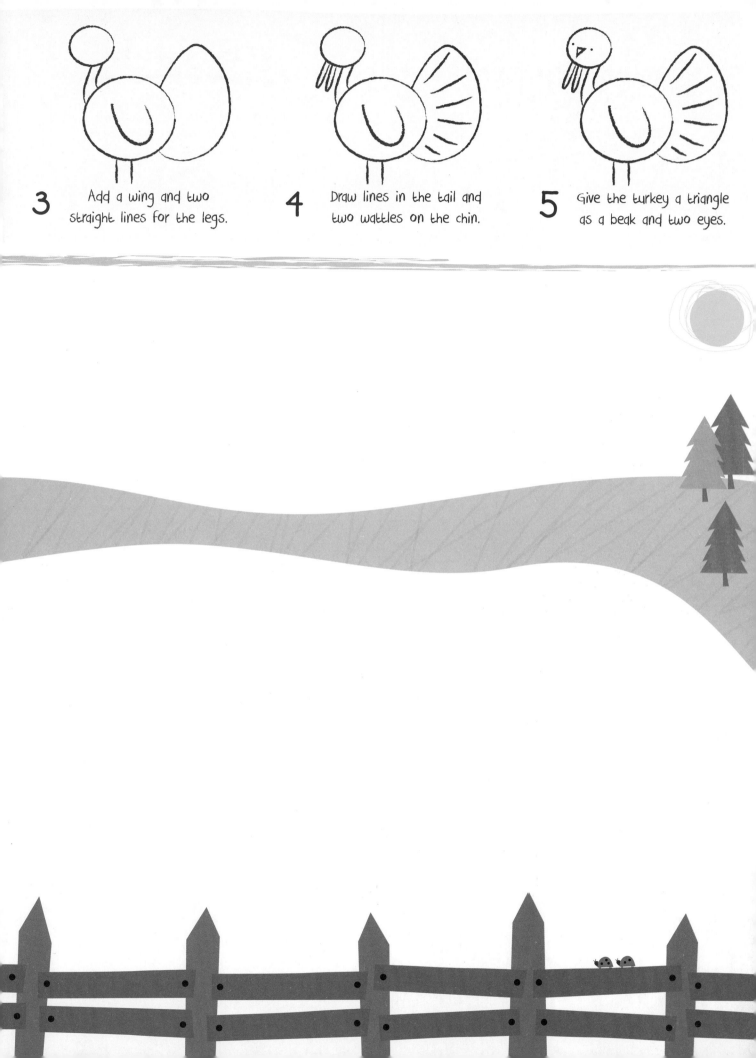

3 Add a wing and two straight lines for the legs.

4 Draw lines in the tail and two wattles on the chin.

5 Give the turkey a triangle as a beak and two eyes.

Grazing **goats**

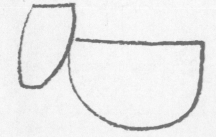

1

Draw a semicircle
for the body and
add a head.

2

Add two little ears
and a tail. Draw four
lines for the legs.

3

Add two long horns
and a goatee.

4

Give the goat two
eyes and a nose.

Smiling **scarecrows**

1

Draw a semicircle
and add a hat.

2

Draw a triangle
for the body.

3

Draw a thin
rectangle for the
pole and add
two arms.

4

Give the scarecrow
a smiley face!

Try drawing your own . . .

Mooing COWS

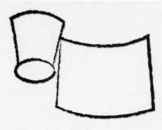

1 Draw a curved rectangle for the body. Add the head and an oval for the nose.

2 Draw two lines for the legs and add two little ears.

Try drawing your own . . .

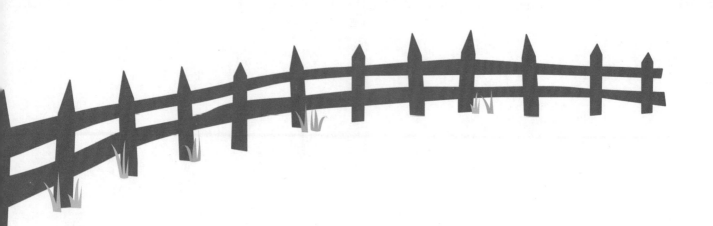

3 Add two horns and a curved line for the tail.

4 Draw spots wherever you want.

5 Give the cow two eyes and two nostrils.

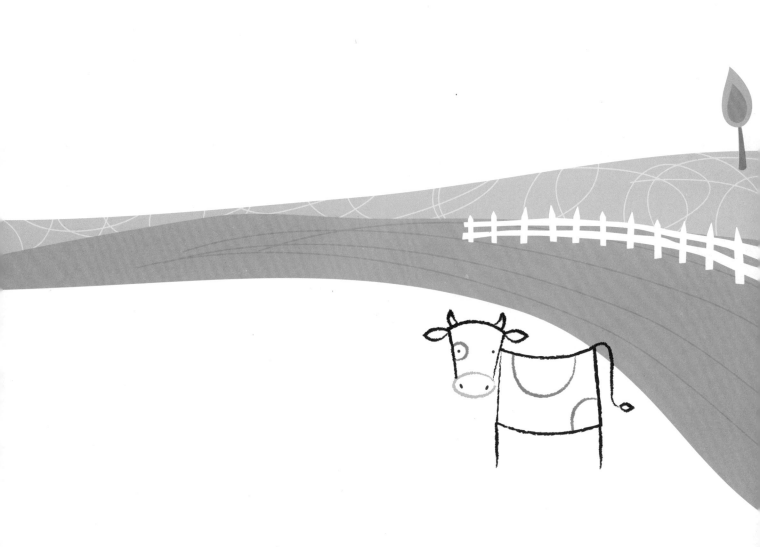

Friendly **farmers**

1

Draw a circle and add a line on top.

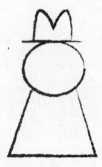

2

Add the hat and the body.

3

Draw two thin rectangles for the legs and add lines for the arms and feet.

4

Give the farmer a friendly face!